Floppy's Colours

Written by Annemarie Young
and illustrated by Nick Schon,
based on the original characters
created by Roderick Hunt and Alex Brychta

OXFORD
UNIVERSITY PRESS

The children had some new paints.
"Gran is coming to tea. Let's
make a huge painting for her as a
surprise," said Biff.

"Let's paint the house where Gran
took us all on holiday," said Chip.

"And the garden," said Anna.

"Can I start?" asked Kipper.

Help Floppy find all the red things in the picture.

Kipper painted a red triangle.
"That's the roof," he said.

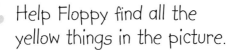

Help Floppy find all the
yellow things in the picture.

Biff painted yellow walls.
"Chip can do the door and
windows," she said.

Help Floppy find all the
black things in the picture.

Chip painted a shiny black
door. Then he painted squares
for the windows.

Help Floppy find all the
blue things in the picture.

Anna painted lots of blue.

"That's the sky," she said.

Help Floppy find all the brown things in the picture.

Kipper painted two brown shapes.
"These are the tree trunks," he said.

Help Floppy find all the green things in the picture.

Anna painted lots of green.
"These are the leaves, and this
is the grass," she said.

Help Floppy find all the
purple things in the picture.

Biff painted lots of purple
flowers.

Help Floppy find all the orange things in the picture.

Chip painted some orange
flowers.

Help Floppy find all the
pink things in the picture.

Kipper painted lots of pink
flowers.

Help Floppy find all the
white things in the picture.

The children painted white lines
to make a fence.

"Surprise, Gran!" said all
the children.

Talk about colours

Which colours did the children use in the painting for Gran?

What animals can you see in the pictures? What colours are they?

What colours can you see around you?

What is your favourite colour?

Mixing colours

You can mix some colours to make other colours.

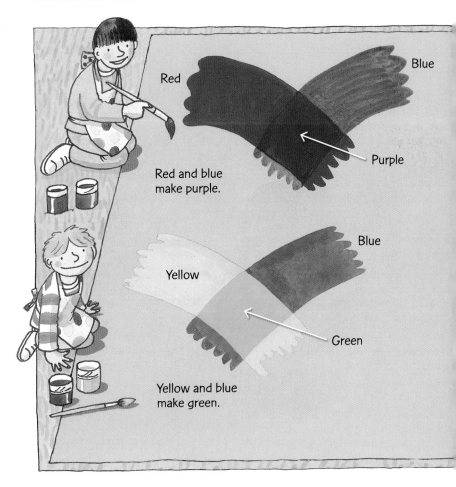

Red

Blue

Purple

Red and blue
make purple.

Blue

Yellow

Green

Yellow and blue
make green.

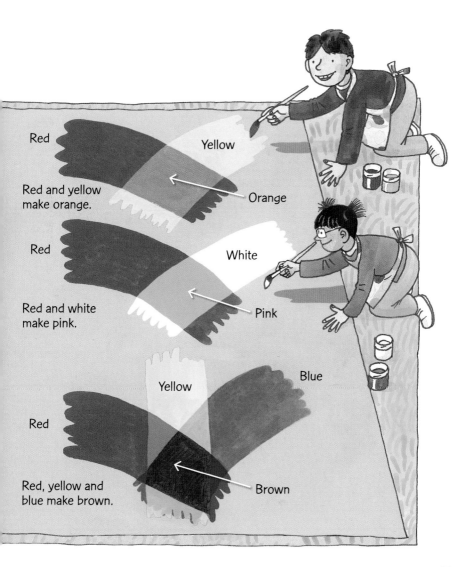

Red

Yellow

Red and yellow make orange.

Orange

Red

White

Red and white make pink.

Pink

Yellow

Blue

Red

Red, yellow and blue make brown.

Brown

29

Mixing Maze

Which colour did each of the children make?